CLASSIC STORIES
OF
·CHINA·

Wisdom Stories

Compiled by Wu Min

CHINA INTERCONTINENTAL PRESS

图书在版编目（CIP）数据

中国智慧故事：英文/伍民编；王国振，汉定，吴晓芳译．－北京：五
洲传播出版社，2011.1(2012.6重印)

（中国经典故事系列）

ISBN 978-7-5085-1903-6

Ⅰ.①中… Ⅱ.①伍… ②王… ③汉… ④吴… Ⅲ.①故事－作
品集－中国－英文 Ⅳ.①I247.8

中国版本图书馆CIP数据核字(2012)第112696号

出 版 人：荆孝敏
编 者：伍 民
翻 译：王国振 汉 定 吴晓芳
责 任 编 辑：王 莉
设 计 指 导：缪 惟
设 计 制 作：苑立静
插 图：李思东

中国智慧故事

出版发行：五洲传播出版社
社 址：北京市海淀区莲花池东路北小马厂6号
邮政编码：100038
发行电话：010-82001477
制版单位：北京锦绣圣艺文化发展有限公司
印 刷：北京圣彩虹制版印刷技术有限公司
开 本：787x1092 1/32
印 张：5.25
版 次：2011年1月第1版 2012年6月第2次印刷
书 号：ISBN 978-7-5085-1903-6
定 价：53.00元

Preface

China has a written record of 5000 years. During the long period, China experienced countless wars, and internal or external turmoil. Several times China was almost wiped out by strong foreign nations. However, China survived, and grew up in strength. China owes this to its rich culture.

A brilliant aspect of the Chinese culture is its philosophy which is full of wisdom.

Wisdom stories have been told for thousands of years, enlightening the Chinese to work wonders. They include some taken in the book, such as *Cao Chong Weighs an Elephant, Eloquent Kong Rong, and Zhuge Liang Graduates.*

Wisdom Stories

CONTENTS

Wisdom Stories

Lu Ban -
The Carpenter
With an Inquiring
Mind

Legend has it that Lu Ban was the first carpenter in China. He is still well-known nowadays. Lots of furniture we use today was invented by him. He also invented tools used by carpenters such as the saw, plane, bevel gauge, and carpenters' sink marker for drawing lines.

There is a story that goes like this: One day, Lu Ban planned to cut down some trees in the mountains to make furniture. While climbing the mountain, he suddenly found some small cuts on his hands. Spots of blood began to flow from some of the cuts. What was the matter? Lu Ban looked around and found that on the mountain slope were some blades of grass with thorns around the edges of the leaves. "Perhaps these thorns hurt me?" he picked up a leaf and brushed it over one of his arms. Sure enough his arm was scratched by the thorns. He never imagined this little tender leaf could have such power. Lu Ban thought, "If this thorn was made of iron, it would be very powerful. Cutting down trees with an axe is so exhausting and time consuming. Aha! Why not make a tool with a thorn-like edge to replace the axe?" He quickly went back down the mountain.

Lu Ban returned home and shared his idea with an iron smith. The smith did as he described. At last, a new tool - the saw came into being. Lu Ban tried it on the trees in the mountains. Indeed it worked very well. Since that time, the saw has been widely used to cut down trees instead of the axe. It was a most useful tool which saved time and energy. We owe Lu Ban a debt of gratitude for this invention.

放牛娃量树

A Child Cowherd Measures the Tree

A Child Cowherd Measures the Tree

A long time ago, there was a child cowherd who herded cattle for his landlord every day. His family only had one ox which was by far the most valuable thing they owned. The child looked after the ox very well and the ox always obeyed his orders. He loved the beast very much. When he herded the cattle for the landlord, he always brought his family's ox with him.

One day, the boy finished his work and brought the landlord's cattle back to the byre. Then, he led his family's ox back home. When he got home, he saw many people around his house creating a great tumult. He went closer to find out what was going on. The landlord was collecting the rent. His family was too poor to pay it. His father was begging for a few more days grace. The landlord was enraged and refused outright.

At this moment, the landlord spotted the ox beside the boy and immediately coveted

it. He tried to snatch the rope from the boy's hand. However the ox was all his family lived for so how could the boy let it go?

The landlord spoke, "I'll give you a chance. Do you see the big tree over there? Tell me the height of the tree in one hour. You're not allowed to cut down the tree. If you can do it, I won't take your ox and I will forego rent for this year. If you can't do it, your ox is mine."

The crowd saw that the tree was wide and high. How could the child's family measure such a tree? There seemed no way out. Nobody had any idea how to do it. The landlord smirked and was just about to take the rope, when the little boy shouted out, "Stop! I can do it." People could hardly believe their ears.

The boy took a straight stick and a ruler. He measured the stick. It was two meters long. He stood the stick up straight and measured the shadow it cast. It was one-third of a meter long. Then he measured the length of the shadow of the tree. It was 8.33 meters long. Then, the boy spoke loudly, "The height of the tree is 50 meters." The landlord didn't believe it. He had the tree cut down and measured it. It was indeed 50 meters high. The landlord was rendered speechless and he had no choice but to leave with his tail between his legs.

Bi Sheng and Movable Type Printing

During the Qingli period (1041-1048) of the Northern Song Dynasty (960-1127) under the reign of Emperor Renzong, there was a man named Bi Sheng who often went to the printing workshop to watch and study how to print books. At that time, woodblock printing was widely used. The characters were cut in relief on a board before being printed on paper. Bi Sheng found that if the book did not need to be reprinted, then those particular printing plates would never be used again; carving woodblock plates was hard work and was very time consuming; if any mistake was made, it was difficult to correct it without discarding the whole plate. So, Bi Sheng decided to try to improve this system.

One day, Bi Sheng was looking at some small clay figures - children, animals, knives and swords. Suddenly an idea came to his head. Wouldn't it be easier to cut each character on a piece of clay and then place the pieces in order on a board for printing? In this way, the pieces could be used repeatedly.

Bi Sheng set to work. He carved the characters needed for a book on some pieces of clay. Each character was cut several times each and certain common characters were cut over twenty times each. After finishing the carving, he fired the pieces to harden them. At last his movable types were ready.

Bi Sheng put the types on an iron plate that was covered evenly with rosin, wax, and an ash-like material. Then he placed the plate near the fire to warm it. When the paste was slightly melted, he took a smooth iron plate and pressed it over the surface, so that the block of type became as even as a whetstone. Then, he spread ink on the in-type characters for printing. When the printing was finished, he again put the plate over the fire to melt in rosin, wax, and ash and then he pushed the types off from the plate. The types could now be used for a number of printing jobs.

If one was to print only two or three copies, this method would be neither simple nor easy. But for printing hundreds or thousands of copies, it was marvelously quick.

Bi Sheng constantly refined his printing techniques and made this invention more and more sophisticated. Afterwards movable type printing spread far and wide and changed the world.

Clever Tong Hui Takes Back the Jade Hairpin

In ancient China, there was a famous scholar named Tong Hui. When he was a child he was admired by everyone for his cleverness.

One day, Tong Hui's mother dropped a bucket into a well to draw some water. She suddenly let out a cry when she drew the bucket from the well. Tong Hui ran over immediately. His mother's jade hairpin had dropped into the well. The hairpin was a gift from his grandmother at a wedding party. His mother loved it more than anything she owned. Now it had disappeared in the water, and she was heartbroken!

His mother carried a long pole and put it into the well to see if she could locate the hairpin. But, she saw and felt nothing in the dark well. The effort tired her out. She looked up at the sun and said to herself, "If the sun could shine down into the well, maybe I would have some chance!" The words gave Tong Hui an idea. He was reminded of a game he played where he reflected sunlight using a mirror. So, he took a mirror and tried to reflect the sunshine into the well. Nevertheless,

whatever he tried, he could not do it with only one mirror. He was very frustrated.

Tong Hui thought for a while and took out another mirror. He placed one mirror near the well, tilting it slightly downward. He held the other in his hands and tilted it upward to reflect the sunlight. In this way, he tried to enable the sunlight to be reflected into the well. Tong Hui adjusted the mirrors several times until finally sunlight penetrated through the clear water and down to the bottom of the well. Exposed to the sunshine, the hairpin clearly came into sight. Tong Hui's mother was overjoyed, "You did it , my son. I can see it!"

"Let's twist a piece of wire into a hook, fasten it to one end of the pole and use it to catch the hairpin," Tong Hui suggested. His mother did as he said and finally managed to get her hairpin out of the water.

Tong Hui's mother was very happy. And when others heard this story, they all said Tong Hui was a most clever boy.

Doctor Hua Tuo - Miracle Worker

In the late Eastern Han Dynasty (25-220), there was a most famous doctor named Hua Tuo.

One day, Hua Tuo was enjoying the cool air in his yard. He spotted a spider under his eave. It was waiting for some unlucky winged insects to fly into his web. A hornet dashed unaware into the web by accident and was trapped. The hungry spider quickly moved toward the hornet and tried to wrap it up in silk. The poor hornet fought desperately not to be captured by the spider. It struggled for all it

was worth.

The hornet with its last energy managed to sting the spider. Hua Tuo found that the spider was swelling up quickly. It seemed that this unlucky creature would have no chance to feast on its prey.

As expected, the spider seemed to give up. It, retreated along one of its silk threads, slowly dropping itself down and finally reaching the flowers. What was the spider doing? Hua Tuo decided to find out what was going on. The spider was slowly moving towards an aloe leaf and with its last bit of energy managed to take a bite of it. The juice flew out of the leaf. The spider dipped his legs in the juice. To the doctor's surprise, the spider totally recovered and the swelling quickly receded. It returned to its web and finally managed to subdue the hornet before tucking into its well deserved meal.

Hua Tuo realized that aloe must have some special qualities. He began to use aloe to relieve the pain of those who were stung by hornets and bees. Sure enough it had magical curative powers. Since then, aloe has been widely used in Chinese medicine and is no longer just a common plant.

Wen Yanbo Uses Water to Get the Ball Back

In the Northern Song Dynasty (960-1127), there lived a famous politician named Wen Yanbo, who, served as prime minister for emperors of four generations. He was very clever and was always ready to help others when he was a child.

Young Wen Yanbo liked football very much. He usually played with his friends in the courtyard. One day, he was kicking the ball around with his friends. One of his friends kicked the ball out of the courtyard by accident. Unfortunately the ball rolled into a

deep hole at the root of an old tree.

All the children rushed over and looked into the hole. The hollow tree was too dark to see anything. The entrance was so narrow that no one could squeeze through. They tried to reach into the hole but felt nothing. Another kid carried over a long pole and tried to locate the ball using it. But the hollow tree was full of bends and curves and it was no use.

What could they do? Nobody had any idea and they just looked at each other almost resigned to losing their ball.

At this moment, Wen Yanbo, who had been quietly thinking, said, "I have an idea. How about pouring water into the hole? The ball will float up." The children thought this idea might work. They returned home, filled basins and buckets and poured water into the hole.

Soon, the hollow tree was flooded and the ball floated up. Wen Yanbo got the ball back and excitedly told his friends, "We made it, now we can get on with the game." All the children cheered.

曹冲称象

Cao Chong Weighs an Elephant

Cao Chong Weighs
an Elephant

During the period of the Three Kingdoms
(220-280), the State of Wei, dominated by
Prime Minister Cao Cao, was the big power
in the northern part of China. Meanwhile , the
State of Wu in southern China was much
weaker. One day, the State of Wu sent an
elephant as a present to the State of Wei in
order to try to show their friendship and
improve relations with their powerful northern
neighbours.

Most of the people in the State of Wei
had never seen an elephant before and rushed

over to admire it. People wanted to know the weight of the elephant. Cao Cao was in a good mood that day. He said to the people present, "I'll reward anyone who can find a way to weigh the elephant."

The crowd were abuzz. How could this huge animal be weighed? Some said, "How about making a giant scales out of a big tree? Then ask Hercules to weigh it." Making such a scales would take a long time and, even if it could be constructed, it would be impossible to lift up the heavy elephant. They thought it over and over and finally shook their heads in resignation and defeat.

At the very moment, a kid ran up to Cao Cao and said, "Daddy, I have an idea." The crowd suddenly fell into silence. Who was this kid? It was Cao Chong, one of the sons of Cao Cao. People knew he was well known for his intelligence even though he was only about five or six years old. Nobody took him seriously including Cao Cao. He jokingly said to his son, "Well, Ok then, tell us your idea, my boy."

Cao Chong said seriously, "You just wait and see."

Under Cao Chong's guidance, a person led the elephant onto a boat near the riverbank. When the elephant stepped onto the boat, the boat sank a lot. A person drew a line on a side of the boat before leading the elephant off the boat. The line was on a level with the water surface. Then, he got some people to carry some big stones into the boat. The boat sank again. When the water surface was even with the line, Cao Chong asked them to stop.

Cao Chong returned to his father and said, "Now, Dad, ask someone to weigh those stones. The total weight of the stones will be the weight of the elephant." The crowd were amazed. No adult had expected that a kid could find such a simple way to weigh the elephant. Cao Cao felt proud and was delighted with his son's performance and his love and respect for him increased even more.

Tiger and Yunnan Baiyao

When children accidentally cut their hands, their parents or doctors will cover the wound with a Band-Aid to stop the bleeding. Why is a Band-Aid so efficacious against bleeding? The answer can be found in the use of *Yunnan Baiyao* as an ingredient in the bandage. *Yunnan Baiyao* is a white-coloured traditional Chinese medicine that is excellent for stopping bleeding.

The discovery of *Yunnan Baiyao* is closely connected with a story concerning a tiger.

During the Guangxu Period (1875-1908) of the Qing Dynasty (1644-1911), there was a doctor named Qu Huanzhang who lived in a small village. He gathered herbs in the mountains. One day, when Qu Huanzhang had finished his herb gathering, dark had fallen. On his way home, he suddenly was confronted with a large tiger hiding in the grass. It was too late to run. Thinking quickly, Qu Huanzhang lifted a big stone and threw it at the tiger. Luckily for him, he hit the tiger a hard blow and the beast was knocked to the ground. It struggled for a while and finally lay there still. To ensure it was dead, Qu Huanzhang poked its head with a stick. The tiger remained motionless. It was late and the tiger was too heavy to carry. He planned to ask his friends to come and help him carry the tiger back the next day.

Next day, Qu Huanzhang, together with his friends, walked to the place where the tiger had fallen only to find it completely empty. The tiger had gone. He realized the tiger must have been still alive. They followed the bloodstains left by the tiger and tried to find out where it had got to. Qu Huanzhang noticed some grass that has been chewed by the tiger. He wondered why a tiger - a carnivorous animal - would ate grass. As a doctor, instinct told him that the tiger was seeking some medicinal benefit by eating this grass. He decided to collect some samples. While the others were still searching the mountain, he started to study the grass at home. He carried out lots of experiments and discovered that the grass had magical curative effective against wounds and trauma. He continued his research until finally *Yunnan Baiyao* came into being in 1908.

Xu Tong
Saves a Tree

In the late Eastern Han Dynasty (25-220), there lived a boy named Xu Tong in Nanchang. Young as he was, he was so clever that he often outsmarted the adults.

One day, he was playing in his neighbor's courtyard. His neighbor was going to cut down the only tree in the yard with an axe and saw. The tree was tall and leafy. He thought what a pity it was for such a beautiful tree to be cut down. He asked, "Why do you want to cut it down? In summer, it can offer us cool shade and in winter, it can shelter us from the strong wind. The whole courtyard looks so much more resplendent with such a tree standing here." The neighbor replied, "As you know, my family is poor and has been beset with misfortune. We invited a *feng shui* master to try and tell us the reason for our woes. He said the courtyard was square, which was like the shape of the Chinese character '口' (meaning 'mouth'), while the tree is written as the character '木'. When '木' is inside '口', the combined Chinese Character is '困'."

"The *feng shui* master said the character '困' means hardship or poverty and had brought bad luck to our family. It was all because of the tree. If I cut down the tree, our luck will change."

The neighbor's words sounded somewhat reasonable, but Xu Tong, after carefully thinking for a moment, came up with a clever idea. He said with a smile, "I have also read such words in the books: The courtyard is square, which is like the Chinese character '口'. If the Chinese character '人' (person) is written inside the character '口', the combined character is '囚' (prisoner)." Xu Tong laughed and said, "Which one do you think is more inauspicious, '困' or '囚'? If you cut down the tree today, there is a good chance you will have to move away from the courtyard and maybe even be a prisoner." The neighbor nodded thinking that what the boy had said made sense.

Xu Tong continued, "If your family pulls together and works hard, you will find ways out of trouble. Don't believe the *feng shu*i master who is just trying to con his way into your house in order to steal your goods." Finally, the neighbor changed his mind and the tree was saved.

Bitter Plums

Wang Rong, a prime minister in the Western Jin Dynasty (265-316), was a very intelligent child when he was young. He was often praised by people around him.

When he was seven years old, he was playing with his little friends outdoors one summer's day. They were talking, laughing and running along the road and enjoying themselves very much.

Suddenly, one child shouted excitedly, "Look at the plums! They look so big and juicy! Come on, guys! Let's take some."

The children ran to the tree. It was indeed a plum tree covered with big, ripe and mouth-watering fruit. They swarmed towards the tree.

At this moment, Wang Rong was walking up slowly, not hurrying at all. Instead he shouted at his buddies, "Stop! The plums are not good to eat!" The children ignored him thinking only of the lovely fruit and left him far behind. Wang Rong's best friend didn't want him to miss out on the fruit so he said to him, "Hurry up! Or you'll get no plums!" Wang Rong answered, "Don't hurry! The plums are too bitter to eat." But his friend didn't believe him and ran off towards the plum tree.

One child nimbly climbed up the tree, picked a plum and wiped it on his clothes. Hardly had he put it to his mouth when Wang Rong arrived, "Don't eat it! It's bitter! " he shouted. The child curled his lip and retorted, "What? Look at this big red plum. How could it be anything but delicious!" Then he took a bite out of the plum. No sooner had he tasted

it than he spat it out, "What a bitter plum!"
The others couldn't believe it. They all picked
plums and tasted them, only to find they were
all very bitter.

The children gathered around Wang
Rong, "How did you know the plums were
bitter?" He replied, "It's simple. See, it grows
by the road and the fruit are all big and red.
If they tasted good, they would have already
been picked by passersby. So they had to be
bitter."

All the children admired Wang Rong,
and the adults, when they heard the story,
said, "There is something about that kid and
he will grow up to be somebody someday."

司马光砸缸

Sima Guang Smashes a Vat

Sima Guang
Smashes a Vat

Sima Guang was a famous politician and historian of the Northern Song Dynasty (960-1127). There were many stories told about him. He was very intelligent and studied very hard when he was a little boy. He liked reading historical books, which gave him a solid foundation for his future compiling of a pioneering reference work in Chinese historiography named *Comprehensive Mirror to Aid in Government*. Thanks to his reading, he set himself the ambition of saving his country. He was well-known for his virtue and erudition.

His story of smashing a vat which was full of water to save his friend has been passed down to us. His calmness and wit impressed those who heard the story. The story goes like this: One day, Sima Guang was playing with his little friends in the back garden of his family. It was a large garden and full of various rare plants. The garden had a rockery covered with flowers and grass. In front of the garden gate stood a big vat full of water which was so deep that it could submerge an adult standing upright. In ancient times, there was no tap water and the vat was used to store water for daily use.

Some of his friends were playing hide-and-seek. They covered one child's eyes with a handkerchief and then hid themselves: some ran eastward, some westward, and others towards the top of the rockery. They were laughing and running, and the entire garden echoed to the sound of their laughter. Also, some other friends were trying to catch bugs in the grass; and there was one child who was trying to find out whether there were any fish in the vat. But the vat was too big and tall for him to reach the edge, so he asked another child to help him. The child held his legs and pushed him up with all his might. However, he pushed too hard and the child toppled over into the vat full of water.

"Help! Somebody!" screamed the boy, struggling in the water. Hearing the cries, the other children rushed over and cried out loudly, "Help! Somebody has fallen into the water!" The vat was too large; the water was too deep, and none of them could find a way to save their friend. It was too late to call any adult. Seeing their friend sink down in the water, they were all terrified. Some ran out of the garden, crying and shouting, to try to find help. At that time, Sima Guang, quiet and calm, bent over the edge of the vat and reached his hand out to the child in the water. But he was too short and weak as he was only a child, and he couldn't pull him out of the water. At a loss what to do next, he chose to run outside to find some help. He suddenly stumbled over a rock as he was running. An idea flashed into his mind: Why not smash the vat with the rock; the water would pour out; then the boy would be saved.

Ignoring the pain in his legs, he picked up the rock and rushed over to the vat. Breathing deeply, he lifted the rock high and using all his strength he smashed the vat. Once, twice... and finally "Clang!" the vat was broken and the water gushed out. The child survived. After a while, some adults arrived and helped the child out. He was saved. The story quickly spread, and little Sima Guang was widely praised for his wisdom and courage.

Zhuge Liang Graduates

Zhuge Liang, as the prime minister of the State of Shu in the period of the Three Kingdoms (220-280), devoted himself completely to the service of his state. There were a lot of stories told about him.

When Zhuge Liang was young, he was a student of Master Sima Hui (widely known as Master Shuijing), a famous scholar. Xu Shu and Pang Tong (both well-known during the period of the Three Kingdoms) were his classmates. All of them were clever and studied very hard.

Three years went by. One day, Master Sima told his students, "It's time for you to finish your studies. There will be a graduation test five days from now. You can begin to prepare for it." The students were nervous. They busied themselves reviewing and reciting what they had learned. But it seemed that the impending exam had no effect whatsoever on Zhuge Liang. He was relaxed and spent every day just relaxing or sleeping late.

Five days passed quickly. The day the exam would be held came. Master Sima said to his students, "You've read a lot of books these three years, but I don't know if you're knowledgeable and intelligent enough yet. So, listen! My examination question is this—the one who succeeds in getting my permission to leave Shuijing Village before noon will be allowed to graduate from here!"

Hearing that, the students stood there in shock. No forms of poetry would be tested. All their hard work of revision was for nothing! They racked their brains about how they could pass this unique exam.

A few moments later, someone shouted out, "Fire! Fire! Run away! Flee!" Master Sima smiled and shook his head. Later, someone ran over and said, "Flood! It's coming down from the mountain! Flee! Hurry up or we will all drown!." The Master smiled and remained silent.

At that time, a servant came over and gave Master Sima a letter. It was from Xu Shu's mother. She was very sick and asked for leave to allow Xu Shu to come back home. Xu Shu read the letter and shed bitter tears. He cried and said that he must go back to see his mother. Master Sima smiled, "You're really good at playacting, but your handwriting has betrayed you. You may not leave."

Pang Tong said, "Master, how did you come up with such a test? How difficult it is! But, it'll not defeat me. If you allow me to go out of the village for a walk, I'm sure I'll find the solution. What do you say." Master Sima smiled, "Don't try silly tricks here. I wasn't born yesterday."

Noon was coming. All the students were as restless as ants on a hot pan, but Zhuge Liang, lay sprawled over his desk, fast asleep and even snoring from time to time. Master Sima couldn't help getting a little angry. He would have kicked Zhuge Liang out if it had happened on another day.

All of a sudden, Zhuge Liang stood up, got hold of Master Sima's clothes and yelled, "You have lead us astray, and intentionally tricked us with your crooked teaching methods. Refund my money! I quit!" How could Master Sima, an eminent teacher and scholar who enjoyed a very high reputation in those days, stand such disrespect and calumny? He shook with rage, "How dare you! I should have refused you permission to be my student. Xu Shu, Pang Tong, show him the door!"

Xu Shu and Pang Tong dragged Zhuge Liang out. At the very moment they were out of the village, Zhuge Liang burst into laughter. The other two were puzzled, and asked what was so funny. Zhuge Liang said, "Now look - what time is it, and where are we?" Xu Shu and Pang Tong suddenly realised their friend's ploy. Zhuge Liang went back to beg his teacher's pardon for his rudeness. Master Sima had seen through the trick just as Zhuge Liang had left the room, but it was too late. He smiled at Zhuge Liang, "You have now graduated, and," he looked at Xu Shu and Pang Tong, "both of you also have now graduated."

孔融奇辩

Eloquent Kong Rong

Eloquent
Kong Rong

Kong Rong was a great writer who lived in the late Eastern Han Dynasty (25-220). At the age of four, he was so considerate that he would leave the big pears in a bowl to his brothers and take the small one himself. In addition, he was a very quick-witted child.

The little boy once went to the capital Luoyang with his father. The then governor of Luoyang was Li Yuanli. As he was a versatile and noble personage in society, and many people went to visit him every day.

Kong Rong very much wanted to meet

Li Yuanli, also. Upon arrival at Luoyang, he asked his father to take him along on his visit to the governor. But the father refused, thinking his son was too young and immature.

Therefore, Kong Rong went to Li Yuanli's mansion on his own. He told the gatekeeper, "Governor Li's family and my family have been friends over many generations. I have come to visit him today. Please pass my message on to him." Hearing that the visitor was an old family friend of his master, the doorman hurried in to report the message. Li Yuanli urged the gatekeeper to invite the guest into the meeting hall, only to find it was a little boy. He asked, "Can you tell me your name, my boy? You've said our families have been close friends for many generations, but I don't know you." Kong Rong stepped forward and made formal greeting to Li Yuanli. Then he answered unhurriedly, "My name is Kong Rong. I've just come to Luoyang, so obviously you don't know me. Speaking of our families' friendship, it is a fairly long story. My ancestor is Confucius, and your ancestor is Laozi. At that time, Confucius was a student of Laozi, which means they had a relationship of student and teacher. This shows we are old family friends."

No sooner had Kong Rong finished his words, than all the other guests in the hall acclaimed his clever reply and praised him as a wonder child. Governor Li was very impressed by the child's wit, saying, "Good point! You are really an amazing child." Kong Rong was thus invited to take a seat of honor.

Right at this moment, Chen Taiqiu, a senior Taizhong official, came in. Seeing a child seated in the seat of honor, he wondered, "Which family does this kid come from?" Others told him what had happened and how clever Kong Rong was. Yet Chen Taiqiu was not convinced. He wanted to see for himself if the boy was really as bright as everyone said. Then he walked over to Kong Rong and questioned him, "I've heard you are very clever. Is that true?" "That's just a compliment, Sir, "replied Kong Rong in a polite way. Hearing these words, Chen Taiqiu was not very impressed, and observed, "I've heard being bright and clever when one is young does not necessarily mean he will be outstanding when he grows up." Others present looked worriedly for Kong Rong's reaction to this slight. Instead of getting in any way offended, the boy took up his cup and had a drink of tea. Then he responded in a casual tone, "I've heard that saying, too. I guess you must have been very bright in your childhood." Chen Taiqiu was aware Kong Rong was implying that he was a failure now. However, he had nothing to say in reply and could only blush in great embarrassment.

A Little Boy of
Waihuang
and Hegemon of
West Chu

In the late Qin Dynasty (221 BC-206 BC), life for the common people was full of hardship due to the cruel rule of the Second Emperor of Qin Dynasty. This led to peasant uprisings across the country. Among the rebel armies, the strongest were two led by Xiang Yu, Hegemon of West Chu, and Liu Bang, King of Han.

One year, Xiang Yu launched an attack against Liu Bang in order to expand his power. When he attacked Waihuang, a city guarded by Liu Bang, Xiang Yu's troops were defeated as they met strong resistance from Liu Bang's forces as well as the civilians of the city. This made Xiang Yu's blood boil with rage. He issued an order to his soldiers, "After you break into Waihuang City, kill all men aged 15 and above in the city."

Shortly afterwards, Liu Bang's troops surrendered under the fierce onslaught from Xiang Yu's army, and Waihuang City was captured. Xiang Yu led his forces into the city. Just as expected, he ordered that all male citizens aged 15 and above should be driven out of the city and be killed three days later. The whole city was drowned in the fear of death. No one dared to try intercede with King Xiang as they were all aware of his horrible temper. An 11-year-old boy, stood out, and was determined to argue with Xiang Yu. After he told this to his relatives and friends, everyone tried to talk him out of doing so, saying, "Xiang was a cold-blooded killer. If you go, you won't make any difference, and might be killed into the bargain." Yet, the boy was so desperate to save his father and brother that no one could stop him.

The boy went to Xiang Yu's military camp alone. On arriving at the gate, he clamored to meet Xiang Yu. The soldiers who guarded the camp gate found it was a boy, and immediately drove him away. The boy refused to leave and started quarreling with them. At this moment, Xiang Yu happened to be walking by. Hearing the commotion, he came over and asked what was going on. The boy then hurried over and stood before Xiang Yu. Seeing the boy, Xiang Yu wondered, "Which family are you from? What do you come to the military camp for?" Raising his head and looking straight at Xiang Yu, the brave child spoke up, "I've heard you're going to kill every man of age 15 and above in the city. What kind of crime on earth did they commit?" "Yes, I will kill them, because they all helped Liu Bang when I was attacking the city. My army suffered greatly. Isn't that a reason good enough for me to kill them?"

responded Xiang Yu.

Hearing this, the boy nodded and said, "So it seems that the talk among the folk about you is right.",

"What kind of talk? Out with it!"

"They say every time you seize a place, you kill all the people there and loot everything valuable," the boy replied. Xiang Yu flared up and roared, "Who said that?

Now! I want to kill him, and if you don't name him, you'll be a dead man, too."

The boy was not frightened at all. He continued, "People were so scared of you that they helped Liu Bang. Now if you kill the men at age 15 and above in the city, you will be living up to exactly what they say you do. Next time you attack Liu Bang's cities, you will definitely meet even stronger resistance from the common people. Think this over, Your Majesty. As your army far outnumbers that of Liu Bang, it will be very easy for you to defeat him. However, once people take his side, it won't be easy for you to win, and I'm afraid...." The boy didn't finish his words, but his meaning was very clear. By this stage, Xiang Yu was staring at the boy in amazement. He couldn't believe that such a profound truth had come out of a child's mouth. He grinned and said to the boy, "You're right. But for your warning, I would have made a big mistake. For one thing, you've saved the lives of the people of Waihuang

City; and for another, you've also saved the lives of my soldiers. I must give you a big reward." After saying so, Xiang Yu ordered the freeing of all citizens aged 15 and above, and rewarded the boy generously.

The rest of the city were very excited to hear the good news. All went to the boy to express their gratitude. Hereafter, once people mentioned this boy, they would affectionately call him the "Little Boy of Waihuang".

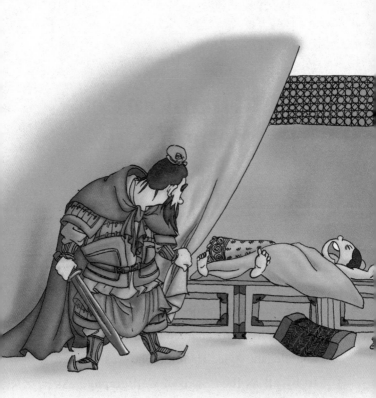

"Drunken" Wang Xizhi

There was a renowned calligrapher named Wang Xizhi who lived during the Eastern Jin Dynasty (317-420). His running script (one of the major categories of Chinese calligraphy) was characterized by a smooth and elegant style. Therefore, he was referred to by all as the "Sage of Calligraphy". As a little child, Wang Xizhi was very bright and sharp-witted. He had begun to practice calligraphy at seven, and was already well famed as a prodigy calligrapher by the age of ten.

At that time, a general called Wang Dun was also very fond of calligraphy. He often took Wang Xizhi along with him wherever he went. One day, he took the boy to his military camp. As it was getting late, Wang Dun told the boy to sleep on his bed.

Since Wang Xizhi had drunk a little wine, he fell asleep as soon as his head touched the pillow. At midnight, he woke up and heard someone talking in another room. "Who is still up at such a late hour?" the boy wondered. Listening carefully, Wang Xizhi got a sudden shock. It turned out that Wang Dun was talking about overthrowing the government with his second in command Qian Feng. Wang Xizhi thought, "Perhaps they have forgotten I was sleeping here. If they realize their music, they will kill me to keep me quiet. What should I do?" After thinking desperately for a few moments, the boy decided to pretend to be dead drunk and he managed to make himself throw up all over the bed. Then he covered his face with the quilt and pretended to be sound asleep.

Just as Wang Xizhi had expected, after his discussion with Qian Feng, Wang Dun realized that Wang Xizhi was still asleep in his bedroom. He said to his man, "This is a matter of life and death. If anyone finds out our plans, not only we but our families will be executed. Let's kill the boy just to be safe."

Holding their swords, the two conspirators walked quietly to the bed on which Wang Xizhi was sleeping. They were about to take his life when they found the bed covered in the boy's vomit. In fact the whole room was full of the smell of alcohol. Seeing the boy was dead asleep, the general hesitated for a second. He put down his sword and sneaked out of the room. It seemed that Wang Dun believed the drunken boy hadn't overheard anything, and thus spared his life.

After Wang Dun and his man disappeared, Wang Xizhi let out a sigh of relief and counted his blessings that he was still alive.

Whose Horse Ran Slowest?

Genghis Khan(1162-1227), the founder of the Mongol Empire, was originally named Temüjin. As a little boy, he lived on the grassland with his father, a tribal leader and a brave warrior who often led his army on military expeditions. Like his father, Temüjin was not only courageous and clever, but also had great strategic ability. This made his father love him very much.

Once when he returned from a successful expedition, Temüjin's father was in such good form that he spent some time drinking and carousing with his soldiers. When they were all well merry with drink, their leader suddenly announced that he wanted to hold a horse race. But this would be no ordinary race. The leader announced that the horse who ran slowest would be the winner. This strange race made everyone very curious and all put down their work in order to watch.

All riders sat ready on their horses. When the race began, each contestant made his horse run very slowly on purpose, so much so that the horses hardly moved a step forward. Some horses even stepped back, and then walked a few steps forward, while others just stood still. This was a picture quite different from the usual galloping storm that was normal in Mongol horse races. Everyone present screamed with laughter, greatly amused by this unique race.

As time went by, it was getting darker and darker. But the riders and their horses were still all at the starting line. The race seemed it would never end, and the audience started to lose interest. Temüjin's father looked a bit worried as he wanted to finish the race as soon as possible.

Seeing his father's anxious look, the 12-year-old boy who had stayed beside him all the time, spoke to him in a low voice, "Dad, I have a good idea to make the race finish quickly." The father, knowing his son was very clever, smiled and asked, "What is it my son?" The boy put his lips to his father's ear and whispered some words. It made the father burst into laughter and clap his hands. Immediately, he told his son to go ahead with his plan.

Temüjin went up to the riders. He told them to get off and exchange horses with each other. The people around couldn't figure out what he was doing. After everyone had exchanged horses, the boy spoke a few words to the riders.

Soon the contest restarted. Upon the signal, every rider whipped his horse heavily. All the horses started to gallop trying to overtake each other instead of staying still as before. The riders finished the race in a very short time. Finally, Temüjin's father announced, "The winner is the rider whose horse ran most slowly." In fact, the winner's horse hadn't run slowly at all.

By this time, the audience began to understand Temüjin's intentions. He had asked the riders to exchange their horses, so that everyone would not be riding his own horse. Then he told all riders that the original owner of the last horse to reach the finishing line would be the winner. Therefore, every racer was aware that if he was the first to cross the line on someone else's horse, he could be the winner. As a result, they all ran like crazy, afraid of falling behind.

Smart Boy

Once upon a time, there were three merchants who were partners in a business. One day, they went to a small village. A beautiful and clear river flowed there with woods and flowers growing splendidly on both banks. With the clean and fresh air, this beautiful part of the world looked like a fairyland. The three men decided to spend some time around the village and enjoy the scenery. Since they were carrying heavy packs on their backs, they wanted to find a place first to put away their baggage.

The merchants saw a farmhouse near the entrance to the village. They went over and found an old lady living there. They entrusted her with their valuables and reminded her, "Please bear in mind that these valuables are jointly owned by the three of us. You can only give them back if all three of us come to you at the same time."

They then left the farmhouse and strolled along the river bank. Suddenly, one of the three suggested taking a quick swim in the river. The other two agreed. As they had brought no towels, they said to the man who had had the idea, "How about going back to the old lady's and bringing back the swimming stuff?" He nodded and headed off.

The man who wanted to get the swimming stuff was trying to figure out how to get all of the stuff from the old lady on his way back. When he arrived at the house and asked the old lady to give him the stuff, she refused, saying, "No, I can't give it to you, unless all three are here. Didn't you tell me that?" The man continued, "Let's go and find them. You can ask them whether they approve or not."

The guy returned to the riverbank together with the old lady. He yelled at his two business partners in the water, "Do you permit me to take back the stuff? Tell the old dame, please." The two bathers shouted to the old lady, "Yes, give it to him. We sent him back to get the stuff." Hearing this, the old woman gave it all to him. The man immediately ran away with all their property.

After finishing their swim, the other two merchants found their partner had still not returned. Realizing that something was wrong, they hurried back to the old lady's house. They spoke quite rudely and unreasonably to the lady, "We sent him to get the bath stuff. How come you gave it him our property? You should pay for our losses. You know, we sweated and toiled to earn that money." They found a judge who ruled that the old lady should be responsible for all of their losses. Unable to afford such a large sum of money, the lady cried her heart out.

A little boy was told about the old lady's misery. He comforted her and said, "Don't worry, Granny. I have a good idea. You go to the judge and tell him the valuables of the three merchants are all at your home now. They can come and pick them up. But they can do so only if all three show up together just as agreed before."

The old lady did as the little boy told her. The judge then informed the two merchants to go to the lady and take their property back. But the man who had fled with their money was nowhere to be found.

Hence, the judge changed his verdict in favour of the old lady.

Cattle Dealer Drives Back the Qin

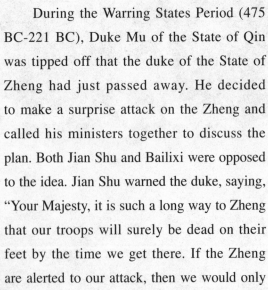

During the Warring States Period (475 BC-221 BC), Duke Mu of the State of Qin was tipped off that the duke of the State of Zheng had just passed away. He decided to make a surprise attack on the Zheng and called his ministers together to discuss the plan. Both Jian Shu and Bailixi were opposed to the idea. Jian Shu warned the duke, saying, "Your Majesty, it is such a long way to Zheng that our troops will surely be dead on their feet by the time we get there. If the Zheng are alerted to our attack, then we would only have a slim chance of success. I'm afraid we can't conceal our attack from the Zheng because we have to march such a long way." Duke Mu would not listen and dispatched his army to raid the Zheng as planned.

Xian Gao, a cattle dealer of the State of Zheng, was driving a herd of cattle to Luoyang to the market when he heard the Qin army marching towards zheng's lands. He was quite worried. On the one hand, it was too late to go back and inform others about the danger. On the other hand, as Zheng was his home state, he couldn't just do nothing.

Xian Gao was a man of intelligence. He thought for a while and came up with a good idea. Then he drove his cattle in the direction from which the Qin army was coming.

At the time, the Qin troops were marching quickly towards Zheng in order not to be discovered by its enemy. One day, a soldier came to the chief commander and reported the arrival of a messenger from the State of Zheng.

The commander was quite shocked, saying to himself, "Has someone let the secret out? Have the Zheng learned about our plan? If they were well prepared for our attack, our raid must fail." He urged his men to bring the messenger in, and asked him hastily, "What do you come here for?" The messenger answered calmly, "I'm Xian Gao from the State of Zheng. Our duke has heard you're leading an army to attack our country. To feast your army and show his hospitality, he sent me to offer you some fat cattle and four pieces of hide. Our duke also mentioned that the Zheng are ready and waiting to meet your army head on. However, we will still provide you with food and guarantee your safety during your stay here."

Hearing those words, the chief commander remained silent for a long while. He thought, "Oh, we are finished. Our plan has failed completely. The Zheng are really on guard against us." With that, he smiled to the messenger and said, "Please send my gratitude to your duke. The Qin and Zheng have always maintained friendship with each other. We are not coming to fight the Zheng. Your duke may rest assured." After the messenger left, the commander said to his men, "We must cancel our plan of attack. They've been alerted. But we can't return empty-handed; otherwise the Zheng people will make a laughing stock of us. We might as well raid the State of Hua before we go back." The Qin troops thus wiped the Hua out and returned home.

The messenger who saved the State of Zheng was none other than the cattle dealer Xian Gao. He drove back the Qin army with his wit, and his brave exploits became legendary in the lands of Zheng.

Sun Bin Rescues
the State of Zhao

During the Warring States Period (475 BC-221 BC), Sun Bin acted as a military adviser to the State of Qi. Since the Qi army won many battles under his leadership, Sun Bin became one of the most famous military strategists of that period.

One year, the king of the State of Wei appointed General Pang Juan to attack the State of Zhao. Under his leadership, the Wei troops defeated the Zhao army several times in succession, and besieged its capital, Handan. Faced with the imminent danger of national subjugation, the king of Zhao State turned to its neighboring State of Qi for help. King Wei of Qi State agreed to help. He had Sun Bin and General Tian Ji command an army to help their neighbor. During the march, Sun Bin spoke to Tian Ji, "The Zhao army is much weaker than the Wei forces in terms of combat capacity. Zhao's general can't rival Pang Juan, either. Moreover, Handan is much more distant from us than from the State of Wei. It is very much likely that Pang Juan's army will have already captured Handan before we arrive. " Hearing this pessimistic analysis, Tian Ji asked anxiously, "You mean we can't save Zhao?" Sun Bin smiled and said, "I have an idea to help them." "What is it? Tell me!" Tian Ji asked. Sun Bin replied, "We must pretend to attack Xiangling. That is an important Wei town. If Pang Juan learns of our attack on Xiangling, he will definitely give up the siege of Handan and return to defend it. At that time, we can lie in ambush and attack them on their way back home.

Pang Juan would be so desperate to save his own country that he will never expect to encounter such an ambush. In this way, we can maybe achieve a great victory." Tian Ji lit up with hope at Sun Bin's shrewd plan. He led the army to Guiling, a place Pang Juan and his troops had to pass by on their way back to Wei. Tian Ji and Sun Bin prepared their army to carry out the ambush. They also told the soldiers to spread the rumor that they were going to attack Xiangling.

Pang Juan and his army were just about to destroy the Zhao when they suddenly heard the rumour that the Qi army was going to attack Xiangling. In a rush, Pang Juan withdrew his troops from Handan and rushed back to try to save this Wei town. On arriving at Guiling, they were ambushed by the Qi army. Commanded by Sun Bin and Tian Ji, the Qi force cut its enemy to pieces and sent them fleeing in confusion. The siege of Zhao was thus lifted, and this battle became known in history as "Besieging Wei to Rescue Zhao".

Sun Bin
Kills Pang Juan
by Using the Stoves

General Pang Juan of the State of Wei
had always come out worst in his battles
against his former classmate Sun Bin. The
mean-spirited general bore a strong grudge
against the great military strategist, and was
determined to defeat the Qi army and capture
its great military advisor Sun Bin. Sun Bin,
who had been fully aware of Pang Juan's
weaknesses, also wanted to wipe him out.

In 341 BC, Pang Juan led the Wei troops
to attack the State of Han. The Han asked
for help from the State of Qi. King Wei of

the Qi State ordered General Tian Ji and
Sun Bin to command an army to rescue the
Han. Given that the State of Han was to the
southwest of the Wei state and the Qi State
was to the northeast of the state Wei, Sun Bin
could not save the Han directly. Instead, he
focused his attention on the capital of the Wei
State, Daliang, which was then defenseless.
Learning that Sun Bin was going to attack
Daliang, Pang Juan hurriedly retreated from
his attack on the Han. When he was back
in the Wei State, the Qi army had already
occupied some of its territory.

Pang Juan and his forces soon won
the battle and the Qi troops fled. When he
took over the camp of Qi, he discovered that
the stoves its enemy had used for cooking
could satisfy 100,000 people. Pang Juan thus
estimated that the Qi forces numbered as
many as 100,000 men. He turned pale with
shock. On arriving at the next enemy camp,
the Wei troops found enough cooking pots
to feed 50,000 people. At the third camp, it

turned out that there were stoves for an army of only 30,000. Pang Juan was extremely happy, and jumped to the conclusion that the Qi troops were so cowardly and scared that more than half of the soldiers had deserted after only three days' fighting. He said to his men, "I'm sure we can wipe them out and capture Sun Bin alive within three days." The Wei soldiers cheered at their general's words.

Pang Juan, thirsty for victory, ordered his army to give chase to the Qi troops through the night. Arriving at the Maling Gorge, they found the path ahead was small and narrow with lofty and steep mountains on each side. Pang Juan sensed something was amiss. At that moment, a soldier came to report, "The mountain path had been blocked by rocks. We can't proceed." He ordered his men to move the rocks away, only to discover the trees beside the path had all been cut down except for a huge one. The general walked to it and found the bark had been removed. Some words seemed to be carved into its trunk.

Pang Juan got his men to light a torch so he could read the words on the tree. They read, "Pang Juan will die under this tree." "We're trapped! Retreat!" he screamed in panic. At this point, the sound of horns was heard all around. It turned out to be the Qi troops, who had concealed themselves beside the path. Now they were firing hundreds of thousands of arrows all at once at their enemy. The arrows burst upon the Wei army like a tidal wave. Pang Juan was hit by a number of arrows. Knowing there was no escape, the general drew forth his sword and took his own life.

Openly Repairing the Plank Roads While Secretly Marching Towards Chencang

In 206 BC, Liu Bang led his men to conquer and occupy Xianyang, the capital of the Qin Dynasty, putting an end to its rule. Xiang Yu, who boasted much stronger military power than Liu Bang, proclaimed himself Ruler of Western Chu, thus breaking his earlier promise that whoever managed to enter Guanzhong (the heartland of the Qin) first would be granted the title of "King of Guanzhong". Liu Bang was quite displeased, but he could do nothing about it and had to swallow his anger. Xiang Yu later conferred the title of "King of Han" upon Liu Bang and granted him some remote infertile lands in Bashu and Hanzhong. Biting the bullet, Liu Bang decided to march westward to build up his strength there.

On Liu Bang's way from Guanzhong to Hanzhong, Zhang Liang, one of his counselors, suggested burning all the plank roads they had past by. Wooden passages were often built along cliff paths in ancient times. According to him, this would prevent Xiang Yu's troops from launching a sudden attack from the rear. It would also reassure him that Liu Bang would not return to Guanzhong to take his rightful title, and thus he might relax his vigilance. Taking Zhang Liang's advice, Liu Bang burned all the plank roads leading to Guanzhong.

Liu Bang's military strength increased greatly in the months after he came to Hanzhong. Eventually he decided to leave Hanzhong and try to wrest Guanzhong back from Xiang Yu's hands. He then entrusted the deployment of his force to Han Xin.

Han Xin was an intelligent and strategically shrewd general who believed that any military move should take the enemy by surprise. He ordered the soldiers to restore the burnt plank roads in a very short time. This was a very arduous task, and many soldiers became exhausted and deserted. This resulted in their military service being prolonged.

Xiang Yu's force soon learned of Liu Bang's movements. Sima Xin, who was in charge of guarding Guanzhong, hurried to send some of his men to seek out some intelligence. On their return, they reported to Sima Xin that Han Xin commanded many soldiers who were repairing the burnt plank roads very quickly, adding that the task had caused great hardship to their men and resulted in a lot of desertions, which was slowing down their progress. Hearing this, he felt much relieved. He believed Han Xin to be an incompetent leader and figured it would take him several years to complete the repairs.

Sima Xin relaxed and lowered his guard.

Actually, in the mean time, Liu Bang and Han Xin had secretly led a larger force to occupy Chencang via a small path, and were marching towards Guanzhong by way of Chencang. As the garrison of Guanzhong was completely unsuspecting, Han Xin and his army were able to rout the enemy and seize all of Guanzhong within three months.

From then on, Liu Bang held the upper hand on Xiang Yu in their power struggle. He soon defeated his rival and established the Western Han Dynasty.

蜀王贪小失大

King of Shu Seeks Small Gains Only to Incur Huge Losses

King of Shu Seeks Small Gains Only to Incur Huge Losses

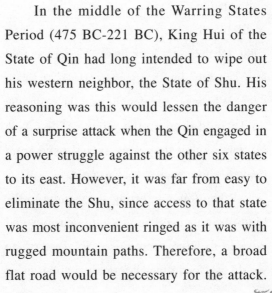

In the middle of the Warring States Period (475 BC-221 BC), King Hui of the State of Qin had long intended to wipe out his western neighbor, the State of Shu. His reasoning was this would lessen the danger of a surprise attack when the Qin engaged in a power struggle against the other six states to its east. However, it was far from easy to eliminate the Shu, since access to that state was most inconvenient ringed as it was with rugged mountain paths. Therefore, a broad flat road would be necessary for the attack.

But to build one called for a large amount of manpower and material resources. Besides, such a movement would alert the Shu and they would raise their guard against the Qin.

After some time, a scout of Qin learned that the king of Shu was a fatuous and incompetent man who was always looking to enrich himself. He reported this information to King Hui. The king soon thought of a cunning plan.

King Hui commissioned several craftsmen to carve five stone oxen. They were so lifelike that they appeared to be real at first sight. He then sent his men to place some gold leaf secretly inside the posteriors of those oxen. Whenever people whipped the oxen, the gold would drop on the ground. This made all believe that they were sacred oxen from heaven whose excrement was gold.

When this interesting story came to the king of Shu's ears, he was quite curious and desired to have such an ox. Every day, he would ask for further information about these legendary stone oxen. One day, a messenger from Qin suddenly came and asked to meet him. The king was much pleased since he could inquire about the stone oxen. The messenger brought him an exciting piece of news, saying, "Our king would like to offer you the five stone oxen as a token of goodwill. What do you say?" Hearing this, the king let out a great peal of triumphant laughter. He hastened to send his envoy to Qin to express his thanks and to have a look at the stone oxen in person.

The Shu envoy came back and told his king, "The stone oxen can really excrete gold. That is undoubtedly true. I saw it with my own eyes. The thing is…it's very difficult to transport them since they are so heavy and the road between Shu and Qin is rough. But if the road could be repaired, the stone oxen could be quickly dispatched." Hearing this, the king beamed with joy and ordered the road to be mended without delay. Soon a broad thoroughfare connecting Qin and Shu was put in place. The king hastened to send his men to transport the stone oxen back.

Learning Shu had fallen into his trap, King Hui of Qin had his general prepared an army of 200,000 men and followed the stone oxen quietly down the newly-built road.

As soon as the stone oxen arrived at the court of Shu, the king ordered his men to whip them. However, not a single piece of gold was excreted. By this time, every one came to realize they had been taken in by King Hui of Qin. Yet it was too late for any second thoughts. The Qin troops, making use of Shu's newly-built road, had already arrived at the gate of its capital. The king of Shu had no other choice but to surrender to the Qin. The Qin thus easily conquered and annexed the State of Shu.

The Empty Fort Strategy: Zhuge Liang Plays Music on the City Walls

In the war between the States of Shu and Wei during the Three Kingdoms Period (220-280), Ma Su, a general of the State of Shu, lost Jieting due to his own negligence. Consequently, the troops of the State of Wei, under the leadership of Sima Yi and his two sons, marched towards Xicheng County which was garrisoned by Zhuge Liang.

Zhuge Liang was commanding his men to transport army provisions, when a spy came to report, "Sima Yi is leading a contingent of

150, 000 soldiers towards us. They are about to arrive in Xicheng County." Zhuge Liang was shocked at the news. He had only 5,000 soldiers, of which almost a half were on ration and forage duty. What was worse, he had not a single general at his disposal. His subordinates were just some civilian officials. How could he possibly resist the attack of Sima Yi? All his subordinates were also stunned at the news. But Zhuge Liang told them, "Relax! I'll go to the city walls to have a look first. I'm sure I'll find a way to force them to retreat."

Looking into the distance from the city wall, Zhuge Liang saw the troops of the State of Wei. They were separated into two columns, marching ahead towards Xicheng County. What could he do in such an urgent situation? After a slight thought, an idea rushed into his mind.

Zhuge Liang ordered his men to conceal all their banners and hide themselves at the foot of the city wall. They were not allowed to move or speak aloud. Anyone who disobeyed orders would be killed. Then, Zhuge Liang gave another order to open the city gates on all sides. Twenty soldiers were sent to the front of each where they disguised themselves as common people just doing some cleaning. Even if the enemy troops arrived, they were not authorized to take any action.

Zhuge Liang took two children up to the city walls. He sat on the balustrades, playing his musical instrument with the smell of sandalwood surrounding him. Before long, the vanguard of Sima Yi's troops arrived. Seeing the situation on the city walls, they dared not move forward any further. Instead, a report was passed to Sima Yi.

Sima Yi was a little mystified. He hurried to the city walls to find out what on earth had happened. He saw Zhuge Liang sitting on the wall, playing his musical instrument, with a smile on his face. The two children standing on either side of him were playing with a sword and a horsetail whip. Outside the city door, over 20 common people seemed to be cleaning the road. It seemed that they didn't even see him and his huge battalion of troops.

Sima Yi suspected that perhaps he was marching into an ambush. Sima Yi hurriedly ordered his men to retreat.

Sima Zhao, son of Sima Yi, asked his father, "I think Zhuge Liang is just making a show. Maybe it is indeed an empty city." Sima Yi answered, "I have fought many many battles with him. He is a man of prudence. He doesn't take risks." In no time, he had ordered all his troops to retreat.

Zhuge Liang couldn't help laughing at Sima Yi's retreat. His subordinates asked him, "Sima Yi is a famous general in the State of Wei, and he led a troop of 150,000 soldiers. Why did they retreat all of a sudden when they saw you?"

Zhuge Liang said, "Sima Yi is a very suspicious man. He knows that I am prudent. Therefore, when he saw I was as cool as a cucumber, he suspected he was walking into an ambush. As a matter of fact, I felt very nervous, but I had no other choice!" Hearing this, all the subordinates admired him for his shrewd plan.

Borrow Arrows in Thatched Boats

During the Three Kingdoms period (220-280), Cao Cao led 830,000 soldiers to attack Sun Quan and Liu Bei in an attempt to unify the country. Sun Quan and Liu Bei decided to ally their forces. Liu Bei sent Zhuge Liang to the State of Wu to assist Sun Quan. Zhuge Liang was a knowledgeable, brilliant and shrewd military strategist. Zhou Yu, who was a narrow-minded man, was jealous of him and was determined to find a way to kill him.

One day, Zhou Yu gathered his subordinates together to discuss some official business. He sent for Zhuge Liang, and asked him, "What kind of weapon is the most powerful in a battle fought on water?" "Arrows, of course." Zhuge Liang replied without any hesitation. "Ah! But we are very short of arrows. I hope you can make 100,000 arrows for us - please say you can do it," pleaded Zhou Yu. Zhuge Liang smiled and said, "I'll do my best. When should I finish?" Zhou Yu asked, "Is ten days enough time?" Zhuge Liang replied confidently, "As war is imminent, three days is enough." Zhou Yu was satisfied with Zhuge Liang's words. He said, "A military pledge must be kept!" "I promise! I'm ready to suffer punishment if I fail." After saying these words, Zhuge Liang signed the pledge.

Zhou Yu laughed to himself when Zhuge Liang left. He thought that it was impossible to make 100,000 arrows in ten days; not to mention three days! I will make him pay for his rash promise, he thought to himself!

Zhuge Liang didn't try to find any workmen. Instead, he asked Lu Su to help him. He said to Lu Su, "I need your help! Zhou Yu intends to use this opportunity to disgrace me and to kill me!" Lu Su replied, "Well you asked for it! What kind of assistance can I give you?" "Please lend me 20 boats, and get your men to place several grass figures on both sides of each boat." Zhuge Liang said, "Remember not to tell Zhou Yu about it; otherwise I will be a dead man." Lu Su agreed.

Two days had passed, and Zhuge Liang did nothing.

On the third night, it was foggy on the water. At midnight, Zhuge Liang invited Lu Su to drink with him on his boat. Lu Su asked, "What can I do for you?" "Come along. Let's harvest the arrows!"

Zhuge Liang ordered his men to link the twenty boats together and sail towards

Cao Cao's camp. When they got close to the target, Zhuge Liang ordered his men to line up the boats, beat their drums and shout out as loud as possible. Lu Su was afraid that Cao Cao would order an attack, but Zhuge Liang just smiled and said, "It is foggy on the water. Everything is a blur in the distance. Cao Cao dares not attack. Don't worry. Just enjoy your drink."

As Zhuge Liang expected, once he heard the shouts and the loud drumbeats, Cao Cao said to his troops, "It is foggy on the water. Launch no attack without counting the enemy soldiers." Cao Cao ordered over 10,000 archers to shoot at the enemies. Immediately, tens of thousands of arrows flew through the air at once.

Zhuge Liang ordered all boats to turn around and line up, so that the other side of the boats faced Cao Cao's troops. When dawn was breaking, Zhuge Liang ordered his men to leave. All the grass men on the boats were covered in arrows.

Zhou Yu sent someone to collect the arrows, which totaled over 100,000. When Zhou Yu learnt where these arrows had come from, he sighed deeply, "Zhuge Liang has such amazing foresight. He is too much for me!"

Cao Gui Awaits
a Third Attack

During the Spring and Autumn Period
(770 BC-476 BC), war broke out frequently.
The powerful State of Qi dispatched troops
to attack the State of Lu. The King of Lu was
horrified when he heard the news, since Qi
was larger and more powerful than Lu, and Lu
had little chance of success.

The crucial battle broke out in
Changshao. The Qi troop beat their drums to
signal the first attack. The Lu ruler was about
to follow suit but was stopped by his general
Cao Gui. He said, "Your Majesty, now it is

not opportune for us to fight back. Would you mind waiting for a moment?" When the Qi troops drew near, Cao Gui suggested that his king order his men to hold their positions instead of fighting back. Meanwhile, archers were ordered to fire at will. The arrows slowed the advance of the Qi troops. The enemy had no choice eventually but to retreat.

Later, the Qi troops beat their battle drums for a second time. Cao Gui once again held back the counterattack, using only his archers to slow the enemies' attack.

When they beat their war drums a third time, the Qi troops lost all morale. At this time, Cao Gui said, "Your Majesty, now, we can hit back!"

With their drums beating out a defiant rhythm, the Lu troops rushed out and successfully defeated the Qi troops. Despite their numerical superiority, the Qi troops were powerless against the onrushing enemy. In no time, the Qi were defeated. The King of the State of Lu was very excited and wanted to order his men to give chase to the enemy. But he was dissuaded. Jumping down from his war wagon, Cao Gui carefully checked the ruts left by the Qi troops. Then, he climbed to higher ground to observe the fleeing Qi troops. Next, he said, "Your Majesty, now, it is time to give chase!"

The King of the State of Lu accepted Cao Gui's advice and finally succeeded in expelling the enemy from his state.

When the war was over, the King of the State of Lu asked Cao Gui why they waited to launch their attack until the Qi troops' third wave of attack. Cao Gui said, "Fighting largely relies on soldiers' courage. After the first attack, the enemy soldiers' morale was at its peak. After the second attack, their morale became a little weaker. And after the third attack, their morale was completely gone. When our army sounded our drums, our buoyant troops had no trouble defeating a dispirited and tired enemy."

"Then, why didn't you want me to give

chase?"

Cao Gui smiled and said, "The State of Qi is so powerful and it has more soldiers and tacticians than we do. I was afraid that they were just pretending to be defeated and were actually laying a trap for us. Therefore, I checked the ruts left by their chariots, and saw their disordered banners. Judging from these, I was sure that they were really defeated. Then I was sure it was Ok to give chase."

Fighting With One's Back to the River

During the war between the States of Chu and Han (206 BC-202 BC), Han Xin was ordered by Han king Liu Bang to attack the States of Wei and Zhao ruled by Xiang Yu.

Han Xin annihilated the State of Wei after winning a series of battles. When his army had recovered from these battles, Han Xin led tens of thousands of soldiers in an attack on the upstart State of Zhao.

As Han Xin's troops had to cross the Taihangshan Mountain, the State of Zhao had time to gather intelligence and make preparations. The king of the State of Zhao ordered his commanding general Chen Yu to gather a force of 200,000 soldiers and station themselves at Jingxingkou, a narrow pass on the Taihangshan Mountain. This was the only access route to the Zhao lands that Han Xin could take. The Zhao troops hoped to use the advantage of local knowledge to counter the enemies' attack there.

The military strength of the Zhao troops was stronger than that of Han Xin and also enjoyed the advantage of fighting on familiar ground. The battle was going against Han Xin. After analyzing the situation, Han Xin found that he had no choice but to lure the Zhao troops out of their positions. It was the only way he could possibly win the battle. Han Xin ordered his men to station themselves 15 km away from the Jingxingkou. At midnight, 2,000 cavalrymen, each holding a red banner, were sent to prepare an ambush near the Zhao encampments. Han Xin told them, "When the Zhao troops pursue us, you rush into their camps and fly our banners. Anyone who successfully makes it will be well rewarded." Then, Han Xin stationed over 10,000 soldiers at a place with a river right behind them. This made his subordinates even more confused, as this was never done when deploying troops. There would be no way to retreat if the battle went badly.

As dawn was breaking, Han Xin personally led his troops in an attack on the Zhao troops. After some fierce fighting, Han Xin pretended that he was defeated and sounded the retreat. The Zhao troops pursued them. Han Xin led his men back to their encampment against the river. The Zhao troops felt that Han Xin's forces were like rats in a hole ready to be slaughtered. That is why all the Zhao troops abandoned their camps and closed in for what they thought was the kill.

The soldiers led by Han Xin joined up with the rest of the soldiers in the camp. There was nowhere to retreat to so they had no choice but to fight desperately.

At this time, the Zhao camps were very weakly defended. The ambushers took the camp easily and replaced the enemy's banners with their own.

The fierce fighting lasted a long time. The Zhao troops saw no hope of victory and retreated to their original camp. But they found that their camps had been taken by Han Xin's ambushers. The Zhao troops had been caught in a classic pincer movement. Their commander was slain, and the king of Zhao captured.

Stories of Wisdom
Trick to Gain Time

During the Three Kingdoms Period (220-280), Sun Quan, king of the State of Wu, sent troops to attack the State of Wei. They laid siege to the city of Xincheng City in the State of Wei. The siege lasted several months. The Wu troops held all the advantages, while the Wei troops suffered heavy casualties.

Zhang Te, a general of the State of Wei, was worried about the situation. The Wu troops were about to attack and capture the city, and his reinforcements had failed to arrive. Zhang Te climbed up to the city walls, gazing in concern at the numerous camps of the Wu troops under the city wall. He thought, "I must find a way to play for time until our reinforcements arrive." Suddenly, an idea flashed into his mind.

Zhang Te climbed to the city wall clutching his official seal. He shouted to the Wu troops, "Listen, I am an officer of the city. We are not able to resist your attack any longer. Many soldiers and officials are willing to surrender to you. But according to the military law of the State of Wei, no piece of land can be abandoned. If we defend the city for over 100 days, the soldiers' relatives will be free from punishment. Now we have defended it for 90 days. If we are given ten more days, I promise that we will definitely surrender to you at that time. Now, I submit my official seal to you as proof of our surrender. Otherwise, we will fight desperately for the lives of our relatives. Think carefully about my words."

Officers of the State of Wu thought he meant what he said. Besides, the Wu troops were tired out about the many months of the siege. Considering the fact that a desperate fightback would probably result in very high casualties, the Wu officers ordered a ceasefire until the Wei troops would surrender as promised ten days later.

Finding that the Wu troops had ceased fire, Zhang Te ordered his men to rest well for the battles to come some days later. When night fell, Zhang Te sent teams to repair the damaged city walls and to make preparations for war. But the Wu troops at this time had totally relaxed their vigilance

Eight days later, Zhang Te appeared again on the city walls but this time he came to declare war on the Wu troops. The Wei troops at this time had amassed a good stockpile of provisions, and above all, they had greatly improved their morale. The Wu troops were taken completely by surprise, and were powerless to resist the attack, and could only retreat.

Finally, Xincheng City was successfully defended and the soldiers in the city were very excited. Zhang Te was generously rewarded by the king of the State of Wei.

Ji Xiaolan Escapes From Drowning in a Pool

Ji Xiaolan was a scholar during the reign of Emperor Qianlong (1736-1796) of the Qing Dynasty (1644-1911). He was well-read and extremely resourceful in tight situations.

One day, Ji Xiaolan was summoned to drink with Emperor Qianlong. The emperor suddenly had an idea to make fun of Ji Xiaolan. He said, "Ji Xiaolan, as you are so knowledgeable, tell me what does "loyalty and filial obedience" mean in our forefathers' eyes?" Ji Xiaolan didn't realize the intentions behind the question and said without much thought, "According to our forefathers, loyalty means that if the emperor orders his minister to die, the minister has to die. Those who follow such orders are loyal ministers. Filial obedience means that if a father asks his son to die, the son has to die. Those who follow such orders are filial sons."

Emperor Qianlong nodded at his words, saying, "Are you my loyal minister?" Ji Xiaolan hurried to answer, "Yes, I am - I am loyal to the Qing Court and loyal to my emperor." Hearing this, Emperor Qianlong smiled and said, "To show how loyal you are to me, go and drown yourself in the Taiye Pool!" Ji Xiaolan realized that he had been tricked by the emperor, but he could do nothing but obey the order. Ji Xiaolan went outside towards the Taiye Pool,while Emperor Qianlong was laughing inside. The emperor was wondering how this wise man would react to his unreasonable request. After a long while, Ji Xiaolan hadn't returned. Emperor Qianlong felt a little regretful and guilty, "I carried the joke a little too far perhaps. I hope Ji Xiaolan has not jumped into the pool." At this time, Ji Xiaolan hurriedly came back. Emperor Qianlong asked, "Ji Xiaolan, I ordered you to jump into the pool. How dare you come back?"

Ji Xiaolan answered, "I did go to the Taiye Pool and was prepared to jump in, when I met someone. Do you know who it was? It was Qu Yuan, the great poet from the Warring States Period (475 BC-221 BC). Qu Yuan asked me why I had come here to drown myself. The reason why he jumped into the Miluojiang River is that his emperor was stupid and fatuous. He wondered whether my emperor was another fatuous man. I told him that my emperor was not fatuous. Instead, he is wise and brilliant. Hearing my words, Qu Yuan advised me not to drown myself, because if I did, my emperor would be believed to be a fatuous man. Taking into account what he said, I decided to come back, as I don't want my emperor to be mistaken as someone fatuous."

Emperor Qianlong knew what Ji Xiaolan said was not true. But he still felt pleased because both Ji Xiaolan and Qu Yuan regarded him as a wise man. He thus said to Ji Xiaolan, "What a silver tongue you have! I hereby spare your life!"

Who Can Eat More Steamed Buns?

During the Warring States Period (475 BC-221 BC), there were two men called Sun Bin and Pang Juan. They studied the arts of war from Gui Guzi, was a renowned expert in all areas of military strategy.

Gui Guzi was good at teaching, and Sun Bin and Pang Juan both studied hard. He always found ways to test their wisdom. He judged that Sun Bin was wiser and was broad-minded, while Pang Juan was adept at strategy but was somewhat narrow-minded.

One day, Gui Guzi asked an unusual question. He took out some steamed buns and said to his two students, "There are five steamed buns here. Now let's see which of you can eat more. Remember that you can only take two steamed buns every time, and that you are not allowed to take another steamed bun without finishing eating the one in your hand." Sun Bin and Pang Juan both nodded.

As Gui Guzi opened the steamed bun container, Pang Juan found that there were only five steamed buns in the container, so he took two at once and began to wolf them down. In contrast, Sun Bin took only one steamed bun and began to eat it slowly.

Before long, Pang Juan ate up his first steamed bun, while Sun Bin had only eaten half of his. When Pang Juan began to swallow his second bun, he stole a glance at his rival and saw that Sun Bin was still taking his time. Pang Juan was delighted at this. He thought, "I am about to eat up my second steamed bun, so I will surely be the winner."

Before Pang Juan had finished his second steamed bun, Sun Bin finished off his first one. He then reached out and took the remaining two steamed buns from the container. Then, there were none left. He smiled and said to Pang Juan, "You have eaten two, but I have three. I win." After saying this, Sun Bin ate his steamed buns. Pang Juan realized that he had lost the contest. With a piece of bun still in his mouth, he was dumbstruck as he gaped at Sun Bin holding the two steamed buns in his hands.

At this time, Gui Guzi came and said to them, "Pang Juan ate fast, but didn't grasp the overall situation. Although Sun Bin didn't eat fast, he grasped the crucial point. Thus, he won." Pang Juan blushed and felt ashamed.

General Tian Ji's Story About Horse Racing

During the Warring States Period (475 BC-221 BC), horseracing was a favorite pastime for the Emperor of the State of Qi. He always asked his General Tian Ji to race with him. As Tian Ji's horses were not as good as the Emperor's, every time, he lost to the Emperor.

One day, when Tian Ji returned home from horseracing, he met Sun Bin who was staying at his home. Sun Bin found Tian Ji in low spirits, so he asked, "What's troubling you, General?" Tian Ji replied, "You know, I raced with the emperor today and lost again. Why am I the loser every time?" Hearing this, Sun Bin smiled and said, "Next time you race, I will go to help you." Tian Ji was delighted and agreed.

Several days later, the emperor wanted another race with Tian Ji. This time, Tian Ji took Sun Bin to give him some help. As at the previous races, their horses were classified into three classes. The very best ones raced together as did the good ones and also the average ones. After Tian Ji had lost all three races, Sun Bin said to him, "General, have another race with the Emperor, I promise you will win." Tian Ji accepted his advice, and challenged the emperor to another race. As the emperor was still flush with his success in the three races, he agreed without any hesitation.

In the first round, Sun Bin advised Tian Ji to use his average horse against the very best of the emperor's. Unsurprisingly Tian Ji's horse was no match for the emperor's. Tian Ji lost the race. The emperor was delighted.

Then, in the second round, following Sun Bin's advice, Tian Ji's very best horse beat the emperor's good one. Tian Ji was excited, and the emperor felt a little uneasy, as he had never lost any race before.

The third round was the deciding rubber. Tian Ji sent his good horse to meet the challenge of the emperor's average one. At last, Tian Ji's horse won. Tian Ji felt on top of the world. The emperor had never expected that result. He asked Tian Ji, "The horses are the same, but how could you win this time?" Tian Ji said, "I don't know, emperor, please ask Sun Bin to tell you."

Sun Bin explained, "Tian Ji's very best horse is not as good as the emperor's, but better than the emperor's good one. The general's good horse is not as good as the emperor's, but better than the emperor's average one. In the first round, the general used his regular horse against the emperor's very best one. Of course, the emperor was the winner. But in the following rounds, the emperor's good horse was no match for the general's very best one, and the emperor's average horse was beaten by the general's good one. That's why the emperor lost the race."

Hearing this, the emperor realized Sun Bin was a rare talent and appointed him as his military counselor. Sun Bin commanded the Qi troops to win numerous battles.

何塘藏杯除奸

He Tang Eliminates the Traitor

He Tang Eliminates the Traitor

During the reign of Emperor Zhengde (1506-1521) of the Ming Dynasty (1368-1644), eunuchs seized power under the leadership of Liu Jin. His power was second only to that of the emperor. But he was not satisfied with this and dreamed of overthrowing the emperor. Many ministers in the Ming Court opposed him, including He Tang, a tutor of the emperor. Unfortunately, however, they didn't know what to do as they had no proof against him.

One day, all the ministers came to

celebrate the emperor's birthday. Liu Jin was there too. He held his head up high as he rode on his horse. When he got down from the horse, He Tang saw a yellow imperial robe hidden beneath his red court dress. At that time, yellow imperial robes could only be worn by the emperor. He Tang was shocked at the scene, "Oh, no!", he thought. "Liu Jin intends to usurp the throne. I must prevent him from carrying through his plan."

After the ceremony, the emperor threw a banquet for all his ministers. He Tang secretly hid a cup when no one was looking. When a eunuch served the cups decorated with the nine-dragon pattern to each minister, he found that one was missing.

At this time, He Tang intentionally shouted, "Who has hidden the cup? Hand it over, otherwise the thief will be sentenced to death if the cup is found on his person."

Liu Jin was startled at his words, as any body search would give him away. He said, "No. Today is our emperor's birthday. Don't spoil the atmosphere. Just go and take another one!"

He Tang said, "If you didn't take it, why not agree to a body search?" He kowtowed to the emperor and said, "I think we should search everyone, and I say let the search begin with your Majesty. All ministers should be searched one after another. The one with the highest rank should be the first to be searched." While he spoke these words, He Tang winked at the emperor. The emperor respected his teacher very much. He realized that He Tang had some plan in mind. He stood up and undid his imperial robes to allow his ministers to check him.

Then, He Tang asked, "Now, who is the next?" "Liu Jin! It is you!"

Liu Jin turned white and beads of sweat rolled down his face. His reaction made him look more suspicious. Liu Jin had no choice but to submit to the search. The moment when his court dress was undone, the yellow imperial robe hidden inside was exposed.

Everyone was stunned.

Although he knew he was in trouble, Liu Jin still put up a struggle. He drew his dagger and thrust towards the emperor. He Tang anticipated the danger, and moved quickly to intercept the eunuch. At this moment, the emperor shouted out, "Seize the traitor!" Immediately, bodyguards rushed at Liu Jin and took him into custody.

At this time, He Tang took out the hidden cup, and said to the emperor, "Your Majesty, it is me who hid the cup."

以假治假

Give the Fraud a Dose of His Own Medicine

Give the Fraud a Dose of His Own Medicine

During the reign of Emperor Zhengde (1506-1521) of the Ming Dynasty (1368-1644), there was a genius called Zheng Tang who came from Fujian. He excelled in music, chess, calligraphy and painting. Zheng Tang ran a calligraphy and painting shop located at the corner of Gulou Street in Fuzhou. He did brisk business, as he sold his products at reasonable prices.

One day, a customer came to his shop, carrying a famous unique painting by Wang Ximeng, the only one he ever painted.

Wang Ximeng had lived in the Northern Song Dynasty (960-1127). The man said, "I urgently need 5,000 taels of silver. Give me the silver and I will leave the painting here with you. I'll be back to get it in three months. At that time, I'll pay you 8,000 taels of silver." As it was a famous painting, Zheng Tang was quite delighted to have a close look at it. He kept the painting and paid the man 5,000 taels of silver.

At the appointed time, the man did not come back. Zheng Tang became suspicious about the painting. He took it out and checked it closely. Unfortunately, he discovered it was a fake. Zheng Tang felt very angry and decided to try to get his own back on the fraud.

Several days later, Zheng Tang invited some men of letters and experts on painting in Fuzhou to examine and appreciate the painting. An old expert on painting came to look at it, as he heard that it was a great masterpiece. All of a sudden, he said with a stunned look, "Zheng Tang, I'm afraid this is an imitation." Zheng Tang replied to the old man, "Yes, it is. I never imagined that I would be cheated after so many years of running my painting business. Today, I want to take this opportunity to warn you to watch out for the fraud. Now this fake painting is in my hands. I won't deceive anyone. I am going to burn it at once." After he said this, Zheng Tang threw the fake into the fire. All the people were filled with admiration for what he did.

Some days later, the fraudster came back to Zheng Tang's shop. He said that he had been delayed by his business, and that he had come today to pay the money to get his painting back. Zheng Tang asked him, "Do you have enough money to pay?" The fraudster thought Zheng Tang was playing for time. Therefore, he took out 8,000 taels of silver and handed it to Zheng Tang. Zheng Tang turned to his assistant and said, "Fetch that painting for him." The assistant did as Zheng Tang said. The fraudster unrolled the painting and found that it was the same one that he had left with Zheng Tang. The fraudster was struck dumb, and took the painting away.

As a matter of fact, the painting burned had been another imitation painted by Zheng Tang. The fraudster thought his own imitation had been burned, so his plan had been to extort more money from Zheng Tang. But to his surprise, he himself had been tricked instead.

摸钟辨盗

A Trick to Find the Thief

A Trick to Find the Thief

Chen Shugu was a wise magistrate from Pucheng County in the Song Dynasty (960-1279). He solved many criminal cases in strange ways.

Once, a rich man had been stolen. He reported the case to the Yamen (a government office). In response, some suspects were arrested.

According to the investigation, the thief had to be one of the suspects. But all of them refused to confess. What's more, there was no clear evidence. It was very difficult to crack the case.

The suspects would have to be released from custody if no evidence was found. Chen Shugu was in a dilemma. He was fully aware that one of the suspects was the thief, and that he would surely flee once released. At that time, catching him would be next to impossible. Chen Shugu made up his mind to find out who was the thief.

The next day, Chen Shugu told his subordinates that he had had a dream the previous night. In his dream, he was told by a god that there was a bell in the temple on the outskirts of the county. It was a magic bell because it would ring if it was touched by a thief. Chen Shugu sent someone to the temple to fetch the magic bell.

Then, Chen Shugu ordered his men to place it on an altar. Three days later, he gave another order to move the bell out to the yard and cover it with a piece of cloth. In addition, he sent someone to secretly smear it black.

All the suspects were escorted to the

yard. They were told about the magic bell, and how anyone who was a thief would ring the bell once he touched it.

Then, Chen Shugu ordered the suspects to put their hands under the covering cloth one by one and touch the bell.

The bell didn't ring from first to last. At this time, Chen Shugu ordered them to stretch out their hands. He saw that all had their hands stained black except for one suspect.

Chen Shugu shouted triumphantly, "You are the thief; confess now thief!" Hearing this, the thief threw himself on his knees in terror, and confessed all his crimes.

The theft had been so frightened at the magic bell, that he didn't touch the bell when he put his hands inside the cover cloth. The other suspects had no fears about touching the bell because they were innocent of the crime. That's why all the other suspects stained their hands black except for the thief. When Chen Shugu shouted out his accusation, he thought that his offense had been revealed and so confessed his crimes.